# MITCHELL on TRUMPET

## By Harold E. Mitchell

## BOOK ONE
### Lessons 1 – 26

## The One & Only Complete Method Written For Trumpet

- **Endorsed by countless professionals and educators around the globe**
- **Focused on establishing & maintaining a strong flexible embouchure**
- **Includes a DVD providing beginners with structured visual guidance**

Special thanks to:

Ollie Mitchell for his tireless pursuit to see his Pappy's work
available for the next generation of aspiring trumpet players.

Herb Alpert for taking the time to express his feelings towards his
teacher's work and the fond memories of the times they spent together.

Chris Tedesco for bringing "Mitchell on Trumpet" to life with the addition
of an instructional DVD, which is second only to studying with Pappy himself.

Jonathon Robbins for his significant editorial contributions & superior engravings

Executive Producer: Tony Santorella
Executive Editor: Jonathon Robbins
Graphic Designer: Carolyn Connors
Studio Professional: Chris Tedesco

SANTORELLA
PUBLICATIONS, LTD.

# HAROLD E. MITCHELL

*January 5, 1898 – August 21, 1985*

**Harold E. Mitchell** was born on January 5, 1898. His professional career took him from the stages of Vaudeville, to the sound booths of the Talkies, to the production studios of Epic Film, and finally to the role of mentor to many young musicians. Mitchell was a highly respected artist and widely recognized teacher. **Pappy**, as he was affectionately referred to by those who knew him was not only an exceptional artist and educator, but also the author of this extremely effective masterwork for learning to play the trumpet.

Mitchell learned to play the cornet in junior high school, but had never intended to become a professional musician. Drafted into the Army during World War I, he was released from service just a few days later when the Armistice was signed. Shortly thereafter, he toured the entire country for 52 weeks by train with a successful musical comedy show. During this extended road trip, he would seek out every major brass teacher of his era including Alfred F. Weldon, Ernest S. Williams, Richard Shuebruk, Dale Stagers, William Thieck, and Herbert L. Clarke.

Upon his return, the Vaudeville era was in full swing. For the next few years, Mitchell worked many live shows and played in the pit for numerous silent movies, stage plays, and musicals. By the time he was in his early 20's, young Harold had now become astutely aware of his ambitions. In a short time, he became the one of the most sought after trumpet players in the Vaudeville and Theater circuits.

In 1927, Hollywood changed forever when the studios learned how to add soundtracks to their pictures. This new technology was a significant advancement in film which became known as the Talkies. The major Vaudeville Theatres in Los Angeles always called Pappy first when they needed a lead trumpet player, so when the film studios asked them which musicians they should hire, Pappy's name was on the top of the list. When he entered his very first sound stage, it was to begin recording for the groundbreaking film, **The Jazz Singer**. The completion of this project was a pivotal moment for film and became the catapult for Pappy's career. Once synchronized sound became the new standard for film, Pappy was already established as the most requested trumpeter in demand.

Over the next two decades, Pappy continued his work in film at all the major studios, including MGM, Paramount, and Warner Bros., and began teaching select students. His film credits include **The Jazz Singer, The Wizard of Oz, Gone with the Wind**, and **King Kong,** as well as numerous Westerns, Disney Cartoons, and other well known films. He became known as the **Dean of West Coast Brass Players** by his peers since he had played first trumpet for every major studio in Los Angeles. Pappy retained his reputation as one of the most devoted teachers in the country and Hollywood's busiest trumpet player until he retired from MGM Studios in 1947. By the age of 49, he had traveled the globe and was widely recognized by musicians, artists, and educators worldwide.

Mitchell actually increased his activity after his retirement, spending the next twelve years writing his method while continuing to maintain a rigorous teaching schedule. His notable students included Robert DiVall (1st trumpet for the Los Angeles Philharmonic), Elden Benge (1st trumpet for the Detroit and Chicago Symphony Orchestras and maker of fine trumpets), Herb Alpert (Founder of Herb Alpert and the Tijuana Brass, and A&M Records), and Pappy's son, Ollie Mitchell, who himself made his own mark in the 60's, 70's & 80's as one of the top studio players in L.A. Pappy also taught Frank Zenzer, who went on to Paramount, Larry Sullivan, who went on to Warner Bros., and Uan Rasey, who went on to succeed Pappy as the 1st Trumpet of the MGM Film Studios Orchestra.

Pappy lived during an exciting time when musicians played a vital role in popular entertainment. It was a nostalgic era of live performances in music and theater. **Mitchell on Trumpet** is the culmination of Pappy's life's work and is highly acclaimed by many professionals, educators, and artists. It still remains to this day as the only complete course ever written for trumpet which stresses the importance of attaining and maintaining a strong flexible embouchure and developing the positive mental attitude necessary to perform proficiently in any playing situation.

# OLLIE MITCHELL

*Harold Mitchell's Son & Studio Artist*

Oliver Mitchell was born on April 8, 1927. This was the same year that his father, Harold E. Mitchell played for the first synchronized sound movie and ground breaking film, T*he Jazz Singer*. When Ollie was just a few years removed from diapers, his father "Pappy" started giving him lessons. As Ollie puts it, "When I was 5 years old, my dad was practicing *Flight of the Bumble Bee* for a radio show. Pappy claimed that I said, 'I would sure like to do that,' so he pulled a cornet out of a closet and that was the end of my normal childhood. Pappy's peers said he couldn't teach his own son and he set out to prove them wrong."

Pappy was still years away from writing his method, but was always collecting notes and ideas, so what better way to test out some of his theories, studies, and approaches than with his own son. Ollie benefited immensely from the strict training he received from his father. It was because of the discipline instilled in him along with a consistent daily practice routine that he went on to become one of the top studio musicians to work in Los Angeles during the 60's, 70's, and 80's.

Ollie turned professional while he was in high school. One of his earliest gigs was playing on the Hoagy Carmichael radio show. He joined the Navy at 18, and was soon playing in the band aboard the U.S.S Lexington. Shortly after his discharge he was playing first trumpet for many well known band leaders including Duke Ellington, Stan Kenton, Buddy Rich, Les Brown, Nelson Riddle, Henry Mancini, the Glenn Miller Band with Tex Beneke, and many others. In 1958, he gave up 40 private students to go on tour with Harry James, but left in 1960 to play lead trumpet on the award winning Fred Astaire special on NBC. He soon became one of the busiest studio musicians in Hollywood.

Over the next two decades, Ollie made a significant contribution to popular music and performed on countless recordings, television shows, and films. The complete resume of Ollie's professional credits is extensive, however listed below are a few notable artists and productions to which Ollie has contributed throughout his career.

- Barbra Streisand
- Barry Manilow
- Barry White
- B.B. King
- Bing Crosby
- Bob Dylan
- Bobby Darin
- Burt Bacharach
- Cannonball Adderley
- Carole King
- Chet Baker
- Dean Martin
- Diana Ross
- Donna Summer
- Ella Fitzgerald

- Elvis Presley
- Eric Clapton
- Frank Sinatra
- Gladys Knight
- James Brown
- Lionel Richie
- Marvin Gaye
- Marvin Hamlisch
- Mel Torme
- Michael Jackson
- Michael McDonald
- Nancy Sinatra
- Neil Diamond
- Neil Sedaka
- Oscar Peterson

- Phil Spector
- Ray Charles
- Roger Miller
- Tom Jones
- Wayne Newton
- America
- Chicago
- Herb Alpert
- Ike & Tina Turner
- Led Zeppelin
- Mamas & The Papas
- Simon & Garfunkel
- Steely Dan
- The Beach Boys
- The Beatles

- Carol Burnet Show
- Hawaii Five-O
- M*A*S*H
- Sonny & Cher
- The Brady Bunch
- The Love Boat
- The Partridge Family
- The Tonight Show
- A Bronx Tale
- Caddyshack
- Cleopatra
- Hang 'em High
- Shaft
- The Exorcist
- The Way We Were

Ollie ultimately retired to the Big Island of Hawaii with his wife of many years, Nancy. In addition to his Hollywood Studio credentials, Ollie had assembled dozens of different bands over the years, and retiring to Hawaii provided yet another opportunity to do so and the *Olliephonic Horns*, also known as *The Big Island's Little Big Band* was born. Ollie boasts proudly with his contagious smile, "The *Olliephonic Horns* is a 12 to 14 piece band that just sort of fell together in the summer of 1995, and we've been playing together ever since. I have to say that I'm having more fun playing now than I can ever remember having at any other time or anywhere else in my entire life."

# Harold Mitchell's Auto Biography

*Transcribed from his own hand written letter to Charles Colin*

June 22, 1974

I started playing cornet in Junior High School in 1914. I was an extraverted kid and frequently took the first part away from better players. Unfortunately, I always found it difficult to hold a steady tempo. My band director didn't realize that I wasn't doing this intentionally, so he often told me to leave the room as he considered me to be a "Smart Alec" for getting faster and faster while we practiced.

In High School, I improved considerably and would play solos in front of the entire school. My music teacher asked me why I was taking commercial courses as she could see the potential I had to be a musician. She went through great lengths to create a four year music course designed specifically for me after gaining permission from the Principal. This unique curriculum consisted of private lessons in theory, sight-singing, harmony, and counterpoint and I even learned the fingerings of most every musical instrument. She also told me that my use of grammar was not very good and she advised me take additional classes in English.

I had a puppy love affair with a cute little blonde who played the piano accompaniment for all of my cornet solos. She would often help me write some of my English assignments, as well. On the strength of her clever work, my assignments received high marks, and I was chosen to write a senior oration. At this point in time, I didn't even know what an oration was, let alone did I know how to write one. To make matters worse, my cute pianist abandoned me, but with the help of the Los Angeles City Librarian, I wrote my senior oration and it was accepted. As it turned out, I ended up playing Herbert L. Clarke's, *The Debutant (Caprice Brillante)* for graduation and I never had to memorize nor deliver my oration.

After graduation, a good friend and I played duets for six hours almost every day. We would play a three hour duet session in morning, and then take a break for lunch and a few games of pool. We would then play another three hour session later in the evening. In the summer of 1917, I formed a small dance orchestra and played a few jobs in Glendale. Every Saturday, I played for "nickel dances" all afternoon and into the evening, which was a wonderful experience. At this time, the First World War was getting heated and there was an opportunity for baseball players and musicians to find employment in Ray, Arizona working in the copper mines. Once I heard this, I left home for the first time and made good money, especially for a kid in a machine shop, while playing in the company band.

My father missed me, and worked hard to find me a better job in order to get his only son closer to home. I went to work in an oil refinery located in Fillmore, California and also organized a beginning band. I gave private lessons on every instrument, and truthfully, I learned more than I taught. My boss just started learning to play the clarinet and he was just as inexperienced in music as I was in the oil business. Then one day, I was reading an article in the newspaper that men were needed for service in the Army. This was the moment that I decided to quit my job to enlist, but my father wouldn't let me go. I was very disappointed that I could not enlist, since every one of my High School friends that had left Camp Kearney for France, were killed during their tour of duty. Feeling as though it was important to move on, I left for Avalon to play in the Catalina Island Concert Band and Dance Orchestra in the summer of 1918. Then, my number finally came up in the draft on November 10, 1918 and I was mustered into the Army with orders to leave from Kelly Field Aviation School on November 12th. As it turned out, the Armistice was signed on the 11th of November and the entire city started celebrating. All street cars stopped and I had to walk all the way home. On the morning of the 12th, I received a telegram which cancelled my orders. I later received a check for $3.00 that included an honorary discharge from the Army.

Some may call it luck when opportunity meets preparedness. As fate would have it, the William M. Morris Agency from New York had a successful musical comedy getting ready to begin its national tour starting from Los Angeles. I auditioned for the gig and was very fortunate to be hired. We played the Schubert, the Klaw, and Erlinger Houses, and performed in most every major city in the United States for 52 solid weeks, traveling over 33,000 miles by train. While on tour, I studied with the best teachers in the country and kept detailed notes along the way.

Upon returning home, the Vaudeville era was in full swing and I was hired to play first trumpet in all the best theaters in town. One of the most interesting experiences I ever had was playing in the pit for Alex Pantages with a six piece Dixieland band. Alex built a million-dollar theater that was quite alive when Dixieland was hot! He was a band leader with a photographic memory and was very experienced with Vaudeville. We played the first show as written, then closed the book and faked the rest. It was not only a fun, but we became the talk of the U.S. circuit.

After a year, I was offered the best trumpet job in town at the Orpheum Theatre, where we were performing the same shows being played at the Palace in New York. This theater gig only required one trumpet with full orchestra. We would play legit standards for fifteen minutes before every movie, followed by three acts of Vaudeville. This was the absolute prime time for live music and I was privileged to have had the opportunity to experience it. Once this gig came to an end, I continued to work with stage bands, silent movies, and musicals for several years. In 1927, an opportunity was available at Warner Bros. Studio to record sound for a new film that included both dialog and music on the same filmstrip. The name of the film was *The Jazz Singer* and little did I know that it would change the motion picture industry forever. The well known composer and bandleader, Arthur Lange hired me to play $1^{st}$ Trumpet after auditioning six other men, who were all certainly qualified, but my experience, sight reading ability, and reputation must have given me the edge. I played alongside of Frank Zenzer, who played $2^{nd}$ trumpet, and Larry Sullivan, who played $3^{rd}$. This became my trumpet section and we played together exclusively on every major film and for every major studio for many years until the union got involved in 1940.

It would take a book to explain everything that happened, but to summarize the events that took place; the union had two significant effects on the business. First, they placed performance restrictions on recording musicians which no longer allowed us to work at more than one studio. This forced the break up our trumpet section that had a stronghold on the Motion Picture Studio Circuit up until then. Therefore, I had to make a decision which was to commit to MGM, Frank went to Paramount Pictures, and Larry chose to work for Warner Bros. I also took Eddie Parks with me to MGM, who happened to be a student of mine at the time. The second thing that resulted from the union intervention was that many great players from New York and Chicago quickly headed westward to Los Angeles, since more jobs became available. One of the better players to come to town was Manny Klein, who played with Eddie and me at MGM. I went on to play for many great films until I retired from MGM in 1947.

I have been extremely fortunate to have enjoyed steady employment for over 30 years as a professional musician. My career is filled with many memorable moments, so I would like to leave you with a funny experience I had with Max Steiner, who was the Conductor at RKO Studios. We were working an all night session scoring a war picture and Max was having trouble with his cues. At one point in the score the orchestra came to a complete stop at which time I was supposed to play a bugle call. This was also the cue for the orchestra to come back in to finish. We went over this thing so many times, that it became very tiring and boring. Finally, Max caught all his cues and was happy with the take, but when it came time for my bugle call, I was sound asleep. Max wasn't upset; he simply dismissed the orchestra and excused all the brass players except for me. He then made me dub in that bugle call for several hours and paid me for every one of them. So the way I look at it, I actually got paid for going to sleep!

Fraternally yours,

"Pappy"

# Endorsements for *Mitchell on Trumpet* . . .

*As one of Mitchell's students, I am not surprised that his method is the most, well-organized approach ever published. I can attest to his all-conquering approach as being the nearest thing to studying with Pappy himself.*

- **Bob DiVall:** 1st Trumpet, Los Angeles Philharmonic ♦ Credited with the Trumpet Theme to TV's *Dynasty*.

*I highly recommend Mitchell's Method as the best approach to performing on any wind instrument. It is truly the most complete method for playing trumpet that I have ever seen in print.*

- **Al Hirt:** Famous Trumpet Virtuoso ♦ Jazz Trumpet Legend & one of RCA Victor's greatest recording artists.

*Seldom does one find a method of study for a wind instrument as thorough as Mitchell's Method for Trumpet. The author, through his many years of experience, realizes the necessity of fundamental training for the trumpet student. All the materials have a definite purpose. I recommend this method with enthusiasm.*

- **Clarence Sawhill:** Highly Respected Educator & Director of Bands ♦ University of California, Los Angeles.

*I have been playing traditional swing and modern jazz professionally since 1973 and am largely self-taught. Upon beginning **Mitchell on Trumpet**, I was amazed at how quickly my reading skills and physical capabilities improved. Mitchell's method progressively trains the ear and his exercises make noticeable contributions to any jazz player's improvisational abilities. Motivational tips sprinkled throughout help to build confidence for playing in any situation and to make one's relationship to the horn more enjoyable. Mitchell shows that serious application to an effective method does pay off. I recommend this marvelous approach for training trumpet players of any discipline; pop, jazz, and classical.*

- **Bob Strickland:** Extremely Talented Jazz Trumpet Performer for close to 40 years from Everett, Washington.

*I played 1st Trombone with Ollie Mitchell in the Harry James Band from 1958 to 1960. We also played together with Herb Alpert's Tijuana Brass. At the same time, I studied with "Pappy" who guided me through his entire method, and I was eventually able to play every exercise at the required tempo. It was a marvelous experience and I never played better. It is important that this method be available to a new generation of brass players.*

- **Bob Edmondson:** Successful Studio Player with the Harry James Band and member of The Tijuana Brass.

*Having used all four volumes of **Mitchell on Trumpet**, I feel compelled to write about them. This is the most comprehensive treatise I've ever seen. My students are having considerable success from all the studies, not to mention the values learned from the inspirational words of wisdom written throughout. This method has made a monumental contribution to trumpet instruction. Pappy, every student should be indebted to you for making these studies available. I can't thank you enough for taking the time and energy to get them in print.*

- **Gilbert Mitchell:** Lieutenant Colonel Conductor of the US Army Band & highly sought instructor of trumpet.

*After going through **Mitchell on Trumpet** with Ollie Mitchell, I repeated the entire method with an associate. Our goal was to outperform each other each week. As a Freelance Musician in Los Angeles, it is necessary to be able to play all styles of Music. I feel that this method is perfect for not only obtaining the tools of the trade, such as High Range, Endurance, Flexibility, and Accuracy, but also in maintaining these skills. I still read a lesson a week for maintenance. Needless to say, I highly recommend this method to all students and professionals.*

- **Bob O'Donnell:** Los Angeles freelance player in demand due to his stylistic ability to play any genre.

*Mitchell's Method is a fantastic, intelligent, and wise approach to learning the trumpet. It shows you what to practice and how to practice. It is sure to develop the needed skills to become a well rounded professional player. It is also filled with words of wisdom, to help you attain the proper mental attitude towards playing trumpet.*

- **Rick Broadwell:** Royal Hawaiian Band, Honolulu, Hawaii ♦ Freelance Trumpeter

# . . . Endorsements for *Mitchell on Trumpet*

Having gone through lessons 46 through 82 from the advanced books in their entirety with Ollie, I would highly recommend **Mitchell on Trumpet** for any brass student. I benefited greatly from studying with both Ollie and Pappy and still use **Mitchell on Trumpet** for my students, as well as myself. I'm very happy to see this great series published again. Thanks to Pappy, it has allowed and will continue to allow many great artists to excel at their craft, fine tune their skills, and become extremely successful studio musicians.

- **Tom Holden:** Professional Studio Musician, Teacher, Educator, and Performer.

I was blessed to have had Harold "Pappy" Mitchell as a teacher for several years. He taught me three basic concepts which were, and still are an important part of being a successful trumpeter and person.

1. **Patience:** With yourself and with the time it takes to achieve what you strive to do.
2. **Perseverance:** Stay dedicated, and work diligently on a daily basis to achieve what may seem impossible.
3. **Progress:** Be willing to pay the price and you will reap the benefits of your efforts.

Pappy taught me that there is no substitute for system and order in all aspects of life. A teacher can help to develop good habits, but it is up to the individual to find the inner drive to become a better person and successful musician.

- **Bill Peterson:** Recorded every style of music from Classical to Cartoons and served as President of Local 47.

**Mitchell on Trumpet** is the most comprehensive method published. It is organized into individual lessons that progress from the beginner to the most advanced players. Each lesson contains studies in tonguing, long tones, scales, chords, technique, and gradually challenges the player for steady improvement. "Pappy's" method for trumpet is not only great for teaching your students, but will certainly improve your own playing as well.

- **Charles Davis:** Successful Studio Musician and Prominent Recording Artist.

I had the distinct honor in presenting a well deserved award to Harold Mitchell from the New York, Brass Conference for earning the respect of his fellow musicians, and providing a continuing source of inspiration to our musical heritage. It is with great appreciation and admiration, that I am bestowed with this honor.

- **Charles Colin:** Director of the NYBC ♦ Respected author and publisher of many great publications for brass.

In my formative years I had the distinct pleasure of studying with "Pappy." He took me through all four editions of his method, **Mitchell on Trumpet**. These four books take you from the very beginning, through the advanced level, and ultimately to the professional level. The exercises give a good solid foundation for the fundamentals of trumpet playing and at the top of each page there is either a knowledgeable tip or inspirational saying from "Pappy." These are all great books! I would highly recommend them to all trumpet players who are in the pursuit of excellence.

- **Ron King:** One of today's Top Studio Musicians and Recording Artists.

**Mitchell on Trumpet** is a magnificent method that will prepare the trumpet player for whatever they may encounter in their professional career. The well designed lessons and melodic exercises cleverly maintain the students' interest while keeping the mind attentive to the most important fundamentals of the instrument.

- **Gary Grant:** L.A. Studio Musician & Producer ♦ Member of the highly acclaimed Jerry Hey Horn Section.

Almost fifty years ago, my teacher Leo De Mers, introduced me to the Mitchell Trumpet Method. Until then, I had only played out of the Arban's book. The thing I remember about Pappy's approach was how musical the lessons were and how it made me use my ear to move from note to note. I remember how much fun it was to play. The knowledge I gained from Pappy's method gave me the confidence to play anything put in front of me. I highly recommend these books to every trumpet player, you will not be disappointed. Thank you, Pappy.

- **Rick Baptist:** Los Angeles lead trumpet player whose credits include *Dancing with the Stars*.

# FROM AN INTERVIEW WITH HERB ALPERT

## JANUARY 25, 2012

I studied with many teachers in my lifetime while establishing a career as a professional trumpet player and recording artist. During this time I made a special effort to seek out those who were respected educators. I guess you could say there was an "A List" of great teachers in the L.A. area at that time and I took lessons from quite a few that left an indelible mark and had a significant effect on me. Harold "Pappy" Mitchell was one.

Pappy was a unique, unusual gentleman who had an extremely disciplined approach, but remained positive and always gave you a feeling of confidence. He seemed to have an endless reservoir of uplifting sayings that would boost your spirits and give you something to think about. I recall that the first order of business, when I walked into his studio on Sunday mornings, was to clean my trumpet, as cleanliness was very important to him.

My studies with Pappy were structured around his thorough, understandable, and well-organized approach. When I later encountered the published version of **Mitchell on Trumpet,** I thought it was exceptional.

I highly recommend **Mitchell on Trumpet** for any serious student as I believe it is an extremely effective method.

# Herb Alpert

Creator of the Tijuana Brass, Celebrated Recording Artist & Founder of the A & M Record Label.

# TABLE OF CONTENTS

——————— END OF DVD SECTION ———————

## ABOUT YOUR INSTRUCTOR – CHRIS TEDESCO

Los Angeles based Trumpeter **Chris Tedesco** has distinguished himself as a jazz soloist, studio player, chamber artist, orchestral player & musician contractor for over two decades. His trumpet can be heard on numerous recordings for movies, television, records, and commercials with some of the biggest names in the business.

Chris' movie and television credits include *Burlesque,* starring **Cher** and **Christina Aguilera, Ironman, Finding Nemo, Road to Perdition, Batman Begins, Best in Show, American Idol, King of Queens, Ellen DeGeneres Show, SAG Awards, Latin Grammy's, MAD TV, Star Trek, Fox NFL, Fox NBA, Monday Night Football,** and many more.

Chris has performed live and on numerous recording projects with many notable artists including *Christina Aguilera, Josh Groban, Michael Buble, Frank Sinatra Jr., Joe Cocker, Dwight Yoakam, Diane Schuur, Tom Jones, Cher, Paula Abdul, Robert Goulet, Shakira, Mel Torme, Sammy Davis Jr., Frankie Valli, Don Rickles, Johnny Mathis, Donna Summer, John Tesh, The Moody Blues, Blood Sweat & Tears, and Lionel Hampton.*

Chris routinely conducts master classes as a clinician at many educational facilities, yet he still enjoys teaching a full roster of private students in addition to maintaining his busy studio and performance schedule.

# LESSON ONE

An **Open Tone** is produced by buzzing your lips while blowing air into the horn without pressing down on any valves. Start with one of the three open tones below, whichever is the easiest note for you to play. The initial goal is to strive for a clear attack and a fully sustained sound. It is perfectly normal for it to take some time to acquire the knack of striking tones properly. The important thing is to be patient and persistent until you can produce a consistently clear sound with ease.

This first exercise uses **Whole Notes** and **Whole Rests**. Soon, we'll explain more about the different types of notes and rests. For now, simply play and count 4 beats for each **Whole Note** and then count 4 beats of silence for each **Whole Rest**. It is important to always count to yourself while practicing.

Play Slowly

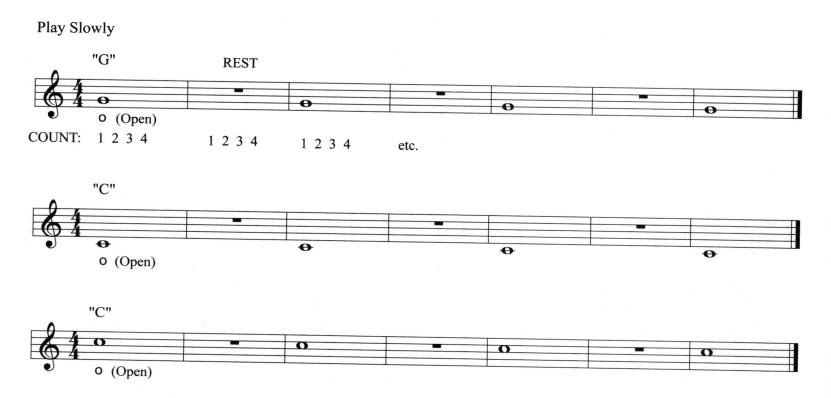

The notes below are not meant to be played. They are simply depicted as a visual aid to show you the first few notes you will learn to play and the letter names and fingerings associated with each of them.

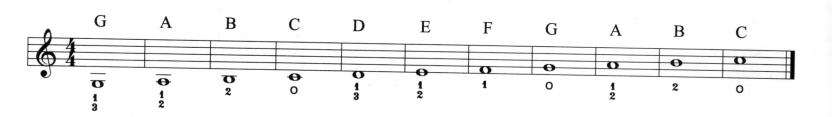

**TIP:** *In order to learn how to read music, the student must mentally say the name of each note, think the pitch, and count the time. Eventually, all three of these actions will be coordinated simultaneously without much effort or conscious thought, and will become quite natural.*

This is the first of many explanations that will appear as you progress through this method in an effort to clarify each note, articulation, dynamic, musical term, or concept when introduced for the first time. Each of these items are also defined in the **Quick Reference Guide** and **Glossary** beginning on page 92.

The first **Articulation** you will notice is called an **Accent** and is indicated by the ( > ) symbol. When you see this symbol above or below a note, strike or attack the note with additional emphasis.

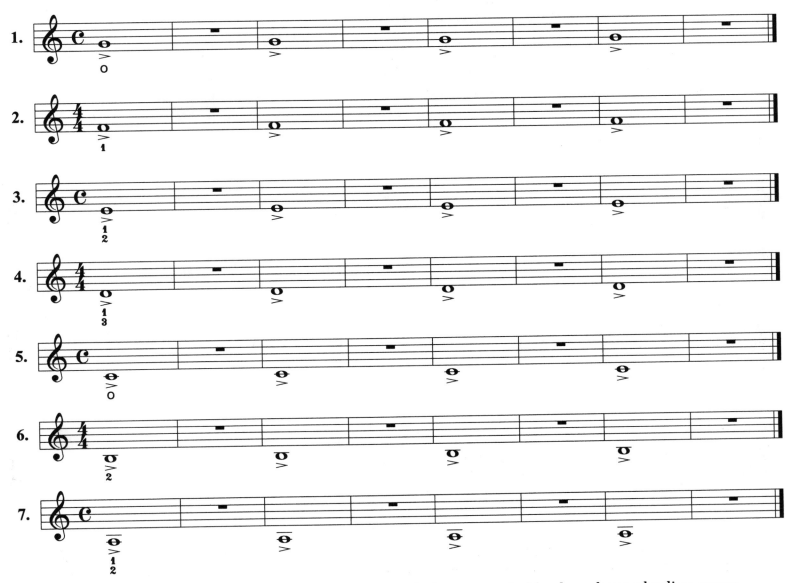

*Fermata* ( ⌒ ): Hold or Pause. When found above or below a note, hold; when above a barline, pause.

*Slur* ( ‿ ): When connecting two or more notes, play all of the notes without an additional attack.

*Sharp* ( ♯ ): Raises the pitch one half-step   •   *Flat* ( ♭ ): Lowers the pitch one half-step.

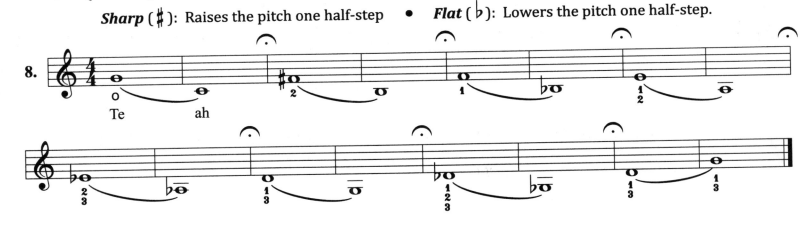

The notes and rests depicted throughout this first lesson are the **Half Note**, the **Whole Note**, and the **Whole Rest**. In **4/4 Time** or **Common Time** ( **C** ), these notes and rests receive the following values:

**Half Note** ( 𝅗𝅥 ) 2 Beats          **Whole Note** ( 𝅝 ) 4 Beats          **Whole Rest** ( ▬ ) 4 Beats of Silence

## Half Notes with Whole Notes

**TIP:** *It is important to rest briefly after completing each exercise.*

## Lip Slurs

## Simple Melody

**TIP:** *These fundamental exercises are most important and must be thoroughly mastered. The beginning student should practice often, but not too long each time, so that the lips may be trained and strengthened gradually, but not fatigued.*

Notice the **Alternate Fingerings** below. These non-standard fingerings produce the same pitch as their standard counterpart. Also known as **False Fingerings,** they are routinely used for the purpose of the **Lip Slur** exercises. When you see one of these fingerings, hold it for the entire group of slurred notes.

# LESSON TWO

*TIP: Good tone quality and intonation are critical first steps in learning the Trumpet.*

15

**TIP:** *It is important to have a regular time to practice and to maintain a disciplined schedule so that no other activities interfere with the time you have set aside.*

## Lip Slurs

## Simple Exercises

In **4/4** or **Common Time** the **Quarter Rest** ( 𝄽 ) gets 1 beat of silence. The **Augmentation Dot** ( · ) after the note adds half the value of the note. In this case, the **Dotted Half Note** ( 𝅗𝅥. ) gets 3 beats.

16

**TIP:** *As you practice each exercise below, listen carefully to every note with a focus on tone quality.*
*Repeat each exercise often until they can be played easily and proficiently, without error.*

## Arpeggio Studies

## Scale Studies

# LESSON THREE

*TIP:* A pure, pleasant tone quality is accomplished by practicing sustained whole notes repeatedly.
Learning to create this pure, pleasant sound is like learning any other skill, so be patient & persistent.

## Chromatic Long Tones

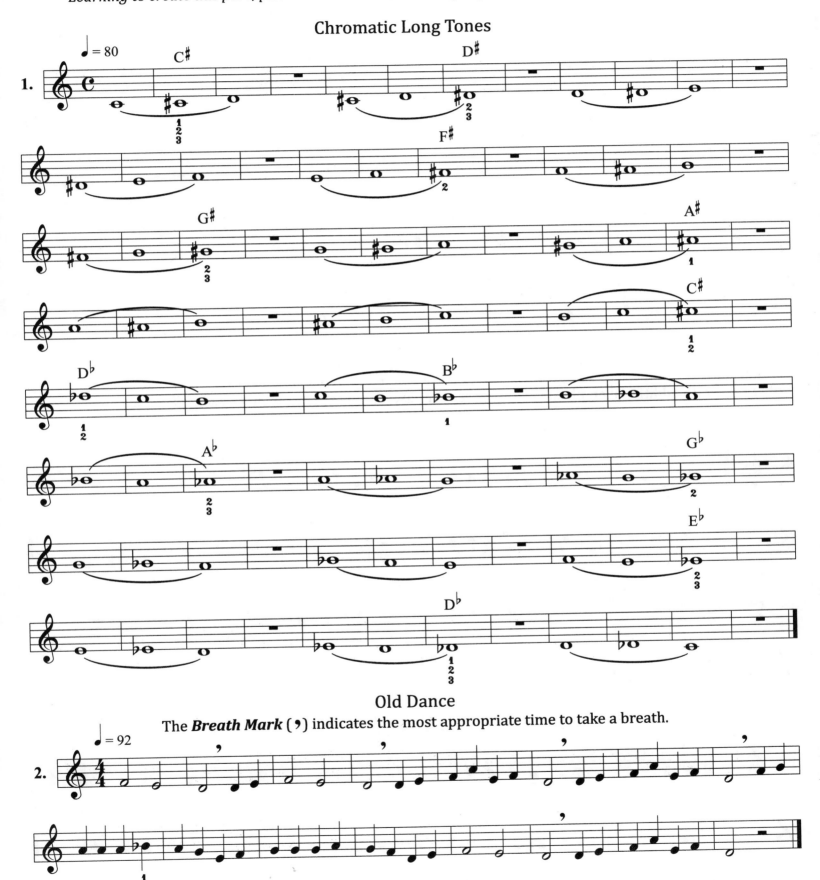

## Old Dance

The **Breath Mark** ( ❜ ) indicates the most appropriate time to take a breath.

18

## Lip Slurs

In the next few examples, notice the addition of the **Accents**, which were originally introduced in Lesson One. You'll see more of these as you progress through the method.  When one appears above or below a note, play that note with additional emphasis.  These three exercises below stress the first beat of each measure.

## Ascending and Descending Exercises in Thirds

### French Melody

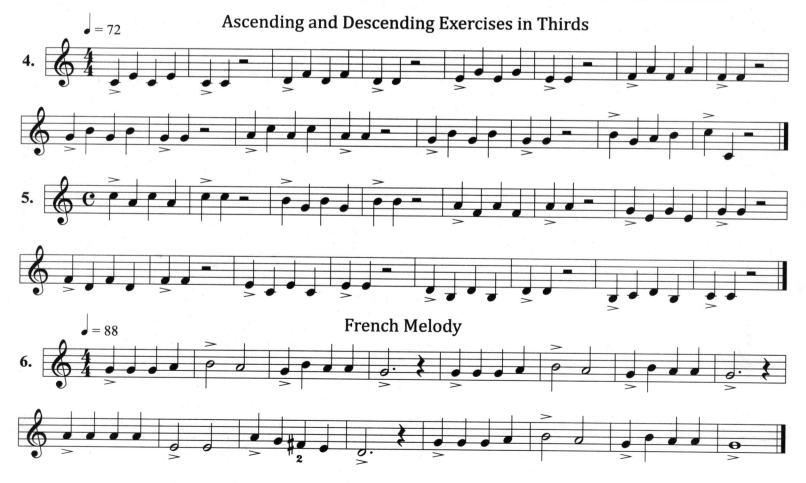

***Syncopation*** is a type of rhythmic pattern that shifts the usual emphasis to a different note.  We'll discuss more about that later, but as you play the next two exercises, notice where the ***Accents*** are placed.

## Fourths in Syncopation

## Syncopated Melody

## Fifths in Three-Four Time

In ***3/4 Time***, each measure has 3 beats. The note durations are the same as in ***4/4***.

## Arpeggios

## Interval Study

## Arpeggios

# LESSON FOUR

***Key Signatures*** are determined by ***Accidentals*** (♯ or ♭) placed at the beginning of each line. Notice where the ***Sharp*** (♯) is placed on line 1. In the ***Key of G Major***, each time an F appears, it is played as an F♯.

**TIP:** *It is important to use the least amount of pressure on the mouthpiece while blowing a steady stream of air. Breathe deeply through your nostrils and the sides of your mouth to fill the lungs to capacity.*

## Slur Exercises

*Reminder: Use your metronome*

## Scale Studies

## Tonguing & Slur Study

## Slur & Tonguing Study

## Rhythm Exercises

*America* & *Exercise 19* are in the **Key of F Major**. In this **Key**, every time a B appears, it is played as a B♭. The complete **F Major Scale** will be formally presented once you have established sufficient range.

## Rhythm Studies

## America
### *My Country 'Tis of Thee*

A **Tie** looks similar to a **Slur**, but it connects two notes of the same pitch, which extends the note's duration.

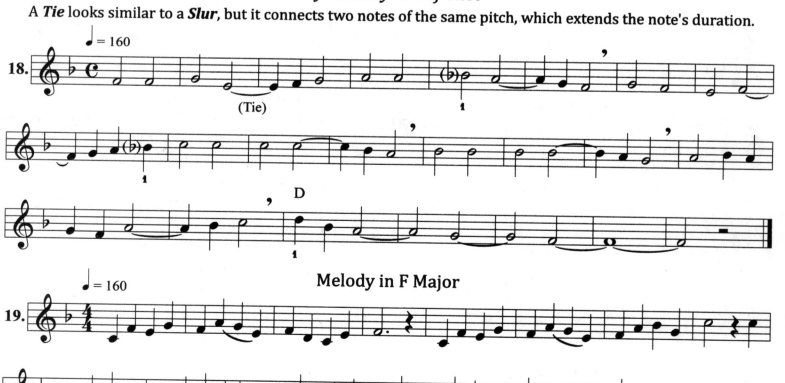

### Melody in F Major

# LESSON FIVE

*Cresendo* ( ◁———————▷ ): Increase Volume - *Decrescendo* ( ▷———————◁ ): Decrease Volume

**TIP:** *If you try to improve a little each day, you will reach your goal before you know it.*

The **Staccato** ( • ) above or below the note shortens the duration of the note.

### Scale Studies in D Major

### Articulation Study

### Study in Fourths

### Chord Study

25

**TIP:** *Articulate each note with the syllables, "Ta," "Too," and "Te" with a solid firm tone, keeping the same volume throughout the duration of the note, unless otherwise indicated.*

## Interval Study with Accents

## Octave Study

## Tonguing & Slur Exercise in G Major

## Rhythm Exercise in F Major

## Rhythm Exercise in G Major

# LESSON SIX

B♭ Major Scale

Chord Study in B♭ Major

Lip Slurs

**TIP:** *The development of your **Embouchure**, or strengthening of the lip muscles, is a gradual process. Every student should guard against strenuous practice. Remember to rest when the lips feel tired.*

**TIP:** *The care & development of your* **Embouchure** *is one of the most important considerations.*

In **4/4** or **Common Time** each **Eighth Note** ( ♪ ) gets one-half (½) beat.

## Rhythm Drills

* Two or more **Eighth Notes** may be joined by a horizonal line called a **Beam.**

# LESSON SEVEN

30

*TIP: Daily practice is vital since muscles acquire strength from regular practice and rest periods.*
*This strength will diminish substantially after a lapse of even a single day.*

## Rhythm Exercise in C Major

## Rhythm Exercise in D Major

## Rhythm Exercise in G Major

## Rhythm Exercise in F Major

**TIP:** *Remember, the attack is initiated by articulating the syllables, "Ta," "Too," and "Te" which releases air to produce the tones. Your tongue should be positioned just behind the front upper teeth.*

## Lip Slurs

## Rhythm Exercises in E♭ Major

## Blue Bells of Scotland

**Andante** (Moderately slow "walking" pace)

# LESSON EIGHT

**TIP:** *The softer you practice, the more supple and responsive your lips will become.*
*As these muscles adapt, tone production will become more comfortable and quite natural.*

### Rhythm Study in G Major

### Study in F Major

### Rhythm Study in D Major

*(Play 6 times, increasing tempo each time)*

### Study in B♭ Major

*(Play 3 times)*

### Rhythm Study in C Major

34

**TIP:** *Everyone makes mistakes, but when you do, it's important to stop immediately and analyze the error you have made.  Uncorrected mistakes will re-surface again, creating bad habits.*

## Lip Slurs

## Finger Exercise in E♭ Major

**Repeat Sign** : Go back to the first forward repeat sign or the beginning and play that section again.

*(Play entire exercise 5 times, observing the repeats each time, as indicated)*

## Melody in E♭ Major

**Andante**

# LESSON NINE

## E Major Scale

## Chord Study in E Major

*Reminder: Don't forget to use your metronome*

## Scale Study in E Major

## Interval Study in E Major

## Lip Slurs

*(Hold same fingering throughout slur)*

**TIP:** *It's normal to have off days, disappointments, and minor set-backs. You must overcome any tendency to quit when progress appears slow and remain focussed on your ultimate goal.*

## Rhythm Study in E Major

## Rhythm Study in E Major
In *4/4* or *Common Time* the *Eighth Note Rest* ( 𝄾 ) gets one-half (½) beat of silence.

## Finger Exercise in E Major

## Rhythm Study in E Major

In *2/4 Time*, each measure has 2 beats. The note values are the same as in *4/4* or *Common Time*.

The *Dotted Quarter Note* ( ♩. ) has the same value as a *Quarter Note* tied to an *Eighth Note*.

### The Dotted Quarter Note Followed by the Eighth Note

### The Eighth Note Followed by the Dotted Quarter Note

### Dotted Quarter Note Melody in F Major

### Dotted Quarter Note Melody in E♭ Major

# LESSON TEN

**TIP:** *All students learn well what they like, and like what they learn well. Enjoy your practice time and the things you play well, but don't neglect the more difficult exercises and studies.*

## Whole Tone Scales
### A *Scale* where every note is seperated by a *Whole-Step*

## Tone Placement Study

**TIP:** *Your practice session will be more productive and rewarding if you have a pre-determined time and place to practice with good light, fresh air, and freedom from interruption.*

## Rhythm Study in G Major

*(Play 10 times, increasing tempo by 4 beats per minute each time)*

## Lip Slur and Fingering Exercise

## Phrasing Study in E Major

40

*TIP: When you see a tempo range for an exercise, start at the slowest setting and repeat the number of times indicated, increasing by 4 beats per minute each time.*

## Rhythm Study in F Major

8.

*(Play 10 times, increasing tempo by 4 beats per minute each time)*

## Rhythm Study in D Major

9.

*(Play 10 times)*

## Rhythm Study in E♭ Major

10.

*(Play 10 times)*

## Rhythm Study in B♭ Major

11.

*(Play 10 times)*

## Rhythm Study in A Major

12.

*(Play 10 times)*

# LESSON ELEVEN

## F Major Scale

## F Major Chord

## Scale Study in F Major

(Play 10 times)

## Interval Study in F Major

## Lip Slurs

(Breathe after 2nd x)

42

*TIP:* *As you increase the tempo for each exercise with multiple settings indicated,*
*do not progress to the next level until you have mastered each one at the previous tempo.*

## Intervals in C Major

## Intervals in F Major

## Finger Exercise in B♭ Major

## Home Sweet Home

Henry R. Bishop

*Syncopation* is a rhythmic variation in a musical passage whereby a note or beat which is not normally stressed is emphasized.   This type of rhythm occurs in *Exercise 15*, below.

### Rhythm Study in C Major

12. (Play 10 times)

### Rhythm Study in A Major

13. (Play 10 times)

### Rhythm Study in E Major

14. (Play 10 times)

### Syncopation Study in E♭ Major

15. (Play 10 times)   1  &   2  &  3 4

# LESSON TWELVE

***TIP:*** *You'll notice that breath marks may be used more sparingly as you progress through the lessons. Scan the music first to look for the best opportunity to breathe when there is no obvious break.*

Notice the introduction of *Cut-Time* or *Alla Breve* ( ¢ ) in *Exercise 8*, below.  This is equivalent to a *2/2 Time Signature*, where there are two beats per measure and the *Half Note* gets one beat.

## Lip Slurs

## March in D Major

## Interval Study in G Major

*(Play twice at each tempo)*

**TIP:** *Correct breathing and breath control are two of the most important functions in the art of playing Trumpet. Controlled use of the diaphragm is a necessity in order to inhale & exhale efficiently.*

## Interval Study in A Major

## Syncopation Study in E♭ Major

## Melody in E Major

# LESSON THIRTEEN

## B Major Scale

## Chord Study in B Major

## Scale Study in B Major

*(Play 9 times)*

## Lip Slurs

*(Play 5 times)*

48

*TIP: Ordinary breathing is an involuntary action. During this function, only a tenth of your air capacity is inhaled and exhaled. In forced conscious breaths an additional eight pints of air can be acquired.*

Interval Study in D Major

Interval Study in G Major

Study in B Major
In *6/4 Time*, there are 6 beats per measure and the *Quarter Note* gets 1 beat.

Rhythm Study in B Major

**TIP:** *Proper breathing is imperative for playing the Trumpet. Inhale deeply to contract the diaphragm. This causes the abdomen to expand which leaves more room for air in largest part of the lungs.*

## Rhythm Study in F Major

*Reminder: Increase tempo each time by 4 beats per minute*

## Rhythm Study in G Major

*(Play 6 times)*

## Rhythm Study in E Major

*(Play 6 times)*

## Scale Study in B♭ Major

*(Play 6 times)*

# LESSON FOURTEEN

***TIP:*** *The two main types of breathing are **Upper Chest Breathing,** (raising the ribs without contracting the diaphragm strongly) and **Diaphragmatic Breathing,** (mainly contracting the diaphragm).*

**TIP:** *The diaphragm divides the lungs from the abdomen and serves as a partition. When the lungs are filled, the diaphragm contracts & the abdomen descends, increasing the size of the chest cavity.*

## Rhythm Study in D♭ Major

*(Play 7 times)*

## Rhythm Study in C Major

*(Play 4 times)*

## Intonation Study in D♭ Major

*(Play 5 times)*

*simile*

## Interval Study in D♭ Major

52

Notice the **Sharps, Flats & Natural Signs** in parentheses from time to time, as in the **March** below.
These **Cautionary Accidentals** are not musically necessary, but simply there as a reminder.

# LESSON FIFTEEN

54

*TIP: To compress the air filled lungs, external muscles of the abdomen are contracted by pushing outward toward your belt-line. Compressed air is vital to vibrate the lips to play in the higher register.*

## Study in F♯ Major

A *Pick-up Measure* or *Anacrusis* refers to a note or notes that precede the first full *Measure*. When this occurs, the value of these notes are taken from elsewhere, usually the last *Measure*, as illustrated in the following melodies.

**TIP:** *Breathing approaches may vary; some use their upper chest while others focus on their diaphragm.*
*For best results, tighten your abdomen as if "grunting" & hold this pressure while playing in the upper register.*

## Interval Study in E♭ Major

## Interval Study in A♭ Major

## Interval Study in F Major

## Syncopation Study in C

# LESSON SIXTEEN

*TIP: Every student should do breathing exercises to get the maximum amount of air into their lungs.*
***Breathing Exercise #1:*** *Lie on your back, inhale slowly and deeply to increase the size of the abdomen.*

## Lip Flexibility Exercise

*Reminder: Use your metronome & increase by 4 beats per minute after you have mastered the Exercise*

## Waltz in F♯ Major

*(Play 4 times)*

58

**TIP: *Breathing Exercise #2:*** *Take a deep breath, hold the air for four seconds and exhale suddenly.*
*This causes the lower abdomen & chest to draw in as the diaphragm applies pressure to the lungs.*

# LESSON SEVENTEEN

**TIP:** *The **Tone and Attack Studies** were created to train the tongue to strike the center of each pitch.*
*It is important to always strive for a clear tone and to attack each note cleanly, with precision.*

## Tone and Attack Study

## Scale Study in G Major

In ***3/8 Time***, there are 3 beats in each measure. The ***Eighth Note***
gets 1 beat and the ***Dotted Quarter Note*** gets 3 beats.

In **4/8 Time**, there are 4 beats in each measure and the **Eighth Note** gets 1 beat.
In a **Chromatic Scale** all notes are separated by one-half step, as in **Exercise 6**, below.

## Two Note Slur Study

## Scale Study in B Major

## Syncopation Study in D♭ Major

## Chromatic Scale Study

*Repeat 4 times at each tempo*

*TIP: **Breathing Exercise #3:** Inhale while standing up until the lungs are filled. Hold the air for two seconds and exhale slowly to allow the abdomen & diaphragm to resume their natural positions.*

# LESSON EIGHTEEN

## C# Major Scale

## Study in Seconds

## Interval Studies in C# Major

## Tone and Attack Study

*accentato*

*TIP:* **Breathing Exercise #4:** *Inhale quickly, fill the lungs and hold your breath for two seconds.*
*Slowly exhale between your closed teeth to create a hissing sound until the air is depleted.*

## Lip Slurs

**TIP:** *Breathing exercises exaggerate normal respiratory movements. This process improves the overall quality of your breathing as you prepare for the ever increasing demands of playing Trumpet.*

## Rhythm Study in C♯ Major

## Diminished Chord Study
Careful and consistent practice of the **Diminished Chords** is essential.
The student is advised to memorize the following Study.

*(Play 10 times)*

## Syncopation Study

*(Play 9 times)*

# LESSON NINETEEN

***TIP:*** *One must learn to fill the lungs quickly, hold the breath, and dispose of it sparingly. The student must also learn to control the muscles involved in deep breathing until it becomes second nature.*

## Lip Slurs

*Reminder: Don't forget to use your metronome*

**TIP:** *The muscles that control facial expressions are also those responsible for developing an embouchure. They not only create the vibration of the lips, but also keep air from escaping from the corners of your mouth.*

## Scale Study in F Major

## Intervals and Scales in C Major

## Syncopation Study in D Major

## Legato Tonguing Study

**Legato** is an articulation that means to attack a note lightly which is normally indicated by the **Tenuto** ( – ).
**Exercise 12**, below, provides a basic phonetic example (Du, Du, Du) of how to create this soft separation.

# LESSON TWENTY

## Tone and Attack Studies

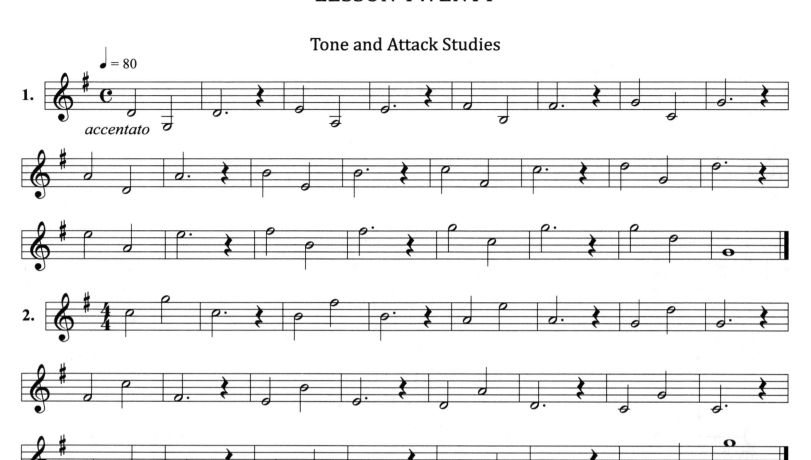

## A Brief Introduction to Minor Keys

The **Key Signature** not only refers to the **Major Key**, but also it's **Relative Minor**. The tone center of the **Relative Minor Key** is determined by the sixth **Degree** of the major scale. There are three types of minor scales; **Natural, Harmonic & Melodic**, as illustrated below. In this case, **D** is the **Relative Minor** of **F Major**.

### The D "Natural" or "Pure" Minor Scale
All notes are played according to the **Key Signature**

### The D "Harmonic" Minor Scale
The seventh note of the scale is raised one-half step

### The D "Melodic" Minor Scale
The sixth and seventh notes of the scale are raised one-half step in the **Ascending** scale, but are lowered to the original pitch in the **Descending** scale.

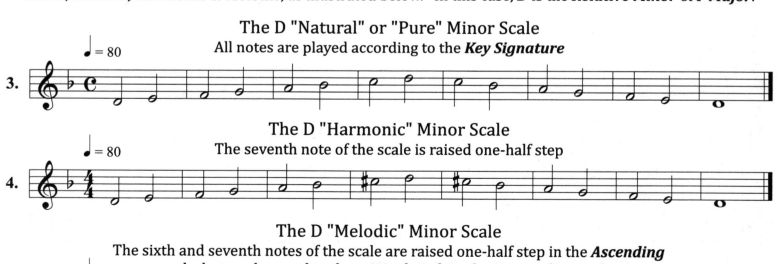

***TIP:*** *Quick inhalation & controlled steady stream of air is required in order to play in all three registers.*
*Self discipline, tenacity, patience, and perseverance are essential for achieving consistent progress.*

## Octaves in G Melodic Minor

## Interval Studies in G Harmonic Minor

## Chord Study in G Natural Minor

## Lip Slurs

**TIP**: *Try to determine which of the three minor scales **Exercise 11** and others that follow are based upon. Remember to look for the **6th** and **7th Degrees** of the scale to see if they have been altered.*

## Scale Study in G Minor

## On Wings of Song

In **6/8 Time**, there are 6 beats in each **Measure**. The **Eighth Note** gets 1 beat and the **Dotted Quarter Note** gets 3 beats.

Felix Mendelssohn

## Pleyel's Hymn

Lento (Slowly)

Ignatz Pleyel

# LESSON TWENTY-ONE

## Tone and Attack Study

*accentato*

## Two Octave A♭ Major Scale

## Chord Study in A♭ Major

## G♯ Melodic Minor Scale

The **Double-Sharp** (𝄪) raises the pitch of the note by 2 half-steps.

## G♯ Minor Chord

The dotted line after the fingerings in *Exercise 9* indicates to hold that fingering for
the duration of the notes that follow, in order to achieve the maximum *Lip Slur* benefit.

## Interval Study in G♯ Minor

## Broken Chord Slurs

## Interval Study in A♭ Major

*TIP:* Lip strain can be averted by using common sense. The wise student will rest their lips frequently and pay close attention to their abdominal muscles & diaphragm, particularly when playing in the upper register.

## Interval and Chord Study

## Nearer My God To Thee

Lowell Mason

## Syncopation Study

# LESSON TWENTY-TWO

## Tone and Attack Study

### F♯ Harmonic Minor Scale

### F♯ Minor Arpeggio

### Interval Study in F♯ Minor

### Chord Study in F♯ Minor

***TIP:*** *Playing Trumpet correctly is achieved with properly controlled breathing, if consistently practiced with diligence. Slower progress and mistakes may be directly attributed to improper breathing.*

## Scale and Arpeggio Studies

*Reminder: Use your metronome & increase by 4 beats per minute after you have mastered the Exercise*

## Arpeggio Study

*(Play 6 times)*

# Rhythm and Lip Flexibility Study

*(Remember, when indicated by the dotted line, hold the fingering for the duration of those notes)*

## One Sweetly Solemn Thought

When the **Meter** changes in the middle of the piece,
observe the rules for the new **Time Signature**.

R. S. Ambrose

# LESSON TWENTY-THREE

## Tone and Attack Study

## Scale Study in A♭ Major

78

**TIP:** *Every student will find growth and progress in the way in which they encounter challenges in their daily practice routine. As with any endeavor, patience & perserverence will help to overcome any obstacle.*

## Interval Study in A♭ Major

## Scale Studies

(Play 6 times)

## Octave Study

(Play 10 times)

**TIP:** *Any advancing student will develop confidence if they insist on accuracy, and never sacrifice tone quality for speed. Haste is one of our greatest enemies as it is the most prolific breeder of bad habits.*

## Lip Slurs

## Rhythm Studies

# LESSON TWENTY-FOUR

## Tone and Attack Study

**TIP:** *Lip pressure on the mouthpiece should be light and evenly distributed. Higher notes may be produced with little pressure if the embouchure and abdomen are used properly.*

## Lip Slurs

## Rhythm Study in F Major

82

**TIP:** *The following **Scale Study** is much like the many others you have encountered in previous lessons. These scale exercises are extremely important in the development of tone, attack & finger dexterity.*

## Scale Study in G Major

*Reminder: Use your metronome & increase by 4 beats per minute after you have mastered the Exercise*

## Syncopation and Modulation Study

When a change of key occurs during a piece, it is called a **Modulation**.
Play the notes from then on according to the new **Key Signature**.

(Play 7 times)

**TIP:** *To achieve maximum progress and endurance, warm up properly, maintain good posture, breathe efficiently, insist on accuracy, and gradually increase your quality practice time.*

# LESSON TWENTY-FIVE

## Tone and Attack Study

## Slur Exercise in Thirds

## Scale Study in B Major

**TIP:** *The secret to success is in reviewing the detail of each exercise and the skills learned previously. Lack of success comes to those who become undisciplined, which results in frustration & stagnation.*

## Arpeggio Study in A Major

## Articulation Study in D♭ Major

## March in E Major
### At a quicker *6/8 Tempo*, count 2 beats per measure.

## Melody in D Major
### At a slower *6/8 Tempo*, count 6 beats per measure.

86

**TIP:** *Practicing a proper attack will train the embouchure to conform with each desired pitch.*
*Every exercise practiced in a consistently, relaxed fashion will produce reliable results.*

### Melody in E♭ Major

### Go Down, Moses

Spiritual

### Turkey in the Straw

Traditional

### Prayer

Carl Maria von Weber

# LESSON TWENTY-SIX

## Tone and Attack Study

**accentato**   *(Reminder: Don't forget to use your metronome)*

## Three Note Lip Slur Study

*(Play 5 times)*

## Lip Slur Study

*(Play 5 times)*

*TIP:* *Practicing should always be done with good posture. The lower jaw must remain still with the chin up and extended. Never allow the cheeks to puff and always maintain a pleasant facial expression.*

## Two Note Lip Slur Study

## Arpeggio Study in B♭ Major

## Scale Study in C♭ Major

**TIP:** *Eight important things to remember: the value of time, success of perseverance, dignity of simplicity, strength of character, obligation of duty, wisdom of economy, virtue of patience, and the power of kindness.*

## Interval, Octave and Attack Study

## Onward Christian Soldiers

Arthur S. Sullivan

# THE MAJOR SCALES

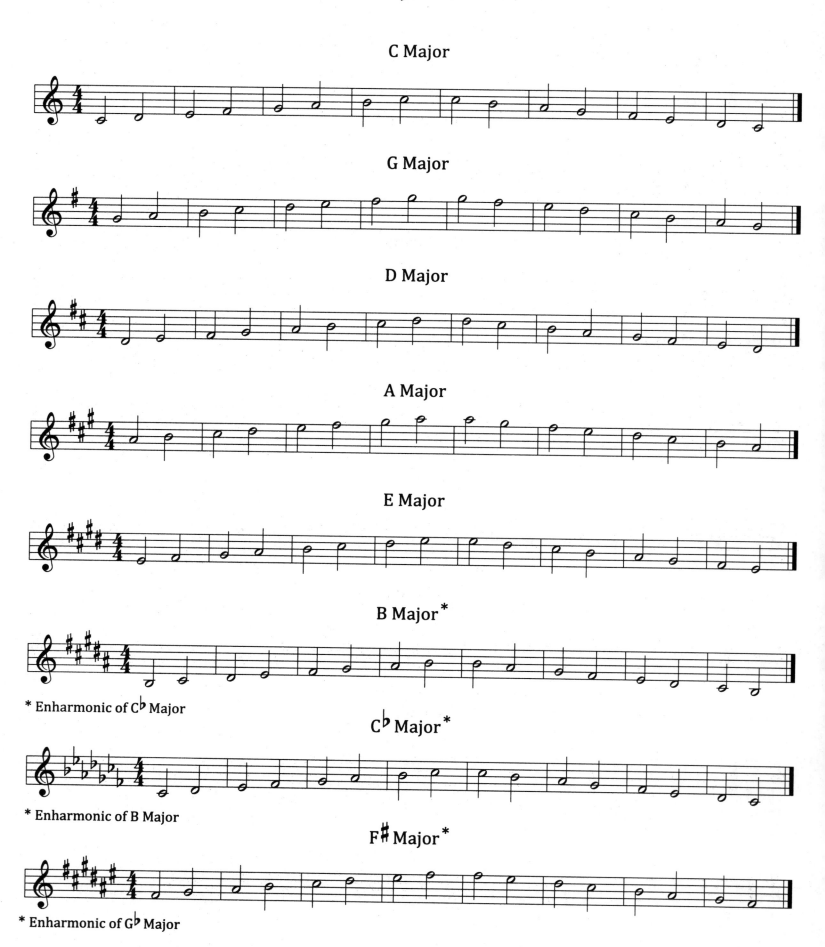

C Major

G Major

D Major

A Major

E Major

B Major*

\* Enharmonic of C♭ Major

C♭ Major*

\* Enharmonic of B Major

F♯ Major*

\* Enharmonic of G♭ Major

# G♭ Major*

* Enharmonic of F♯ Major

# C♯ Major*

* Enharmonic of D♭ Major

# D♭ Major*

* Enharmonic of C♯ Major

# A♭ Major

# E♭ Major

# B♭ Major

# F Major

# C Major

# QUICK REFERENCE GUIDE

## Accidentals, Dynamics, Articulations & Miscellaneous Notation

♯   Sharp: Raises the pitch one-half step.

♭   Flat: Lowers the pitch one-half step.

♮   Natural: Restores the note to an unaltered state.

×   Double Sharp: Raises the pitch two half-steps.

♭♭   Double Flat: Lowers the pitch two half-steps.

(♯)   Cautionary Sharp: Appears simply as a reminder.

(♭)   Cautionary Flat: Appears simply as a reminder.

(♮)   Cautionary Natural: Appears simply as a reminder.

*pp*   Pianissimo: Play very softly.

*p*   Piano: Play softly.

*mp*   Mezzo-piano: Play moderately softly.

*mf*   Mezzo-forte: Play moderately loudly.

*f*   Forte: Play loudly.

*ff*   Fortissimo: Play very loudly.

*sfz*   Sforzando: A forceful, sudden accent.

*sfp*   Sforzando-piano: Strong accent, then soft.

*fp*   Forte-piano: Loud, then immediately soft.

Crescendo (*cresc.*): A musical symbol which means to gradually increase the volume.

Decrescendo (*decresc.*): A musical symbol which means to gradually decrease the volume.

>   Accent: When seen above or below a note, strike or attack the note with authority and emphasis.

Λ   Marcato (as written above the note): Indicates a strong attack followed by an immediate decay.

V   Marcato (as written below the note): Indicates a strong attack followed by an immediate decay.

·   Staccato: Written above or below, it shortens the duration of the note, but does not affect the attack.

—   Tenuto (Legato): Attack the note softly with a subtle separation and hold for it's full duration.

,   Breath Mark: Seen above the staff, it indicates the most appropriate time to take a breath.

//   Caesura: Indicates a brief, but complete pause, during which musical time is not counted.

⌒   Fermata: Hold the note longer than it's full value; usually determined by the conductor or performer.

 Tie: The curved line connecting two notes of the same pitch. Hold the first note continuously, for the value of both notes combined. More than two tied notes may occur in succession.

Slur: Looking similar to the Tie, the Slur appears over the course of two more more notes of different pitches. Play all of the notes smoothly, without attacking each individual note.

# QUICK REFERENCE GUIDE

## Barlines and Repeats

**Single Barline:** The thin vertical line though the staff which divides the piece into Measures.

**Double Barline:** Two thin vertical lines through the staff which usually indicates the end of a section.

**Final Double Barline:** With a thick second vertical line, it indicates the end of the piece or movement.

**Backward Repeat Sign:** Go back to the nearest Forward Repeat or beginning & play the section again.

**Forward Repeat Sign:** Indicates the beginning of a section that is to be played more than once.

**First & Second Ending Repeat:** When reaching the Backward Repeat Sign in the First Ending, go back to the nearest Forward Repeat (or beginning) and play the section again, this time skipping the First Ending & proceeding directly to the Second Ending.

**D.C. al Fine**   Go back to the beginning, this time skipping repeats, and stop when you reach the Fine.

**D.C. al Coda**   Go back to the beginning, skipping repeats, then jump to the Coda when you reach, To Coda.

**D.S. al Fine**   Go back to the Segno (see below), skipping repeats, and stop when you reach the Fine.

**D.S. al Coda**   Go back to the Segno, skipping repeats, then jump to the Coda when you reach, To Coda.

**To Coda** ⊕   After having repeated the section (as per any of the above), go directly to the Coda.

**Fine**   Marks the conclusion of the piece or movement after having observed a D.C. or D.S. repeat.

𝄋   Segno (Sign): Marks the point at which to begin the repeated section after observing a D.S. repeat.

⊕   Marks the start of the Coda, the section of varying length which usually concludes a piece or movement.

𝄎   Repeat the preceding measure, or when appearing as **2** / repeat the preceding two measures.

### Example of the various Musical Elements as they might appear on the Staff

# GLOSSARY OF MUSIC TERMS

**Accent:** Usually indicated by ( > ), an emphasis placed on a particular note, typically most pronounced on the attack.

**Accentato:** Meaning, "accented," play each note as if there were an accent mark written above or below.

**Accidental:** A Symbol (sharp, flat, or natural sign) before the note that either raises, lowers, or restores the pitch.

**Adagio:** Meaning, "at ease," it is a Slow Tempo indication that is equal to a range of approximately 66 - 76 bpm.

**Alla Breve:** Also referred to as Cut Time ( ₵ ), it is the equivilent of a 2/2 Time Signature and often used in Marches.

**Allegro:** Meaning, "joyful," it indicates a lively and fast Tempo range of approximately 120 - 140 bpm.

**Anacrusis:** Note or notes which precede the first full measure in a piece (also called "pickup" or "pickup measure").

**Andante:** Literally, "at a walking pace," it indicates a Tempo in the range of approximately 76 -108 bpm.

**Arpeggio:** From the Italian term meaning, "to play on a harp," the notes of a chord are played one after the other.

**Articulation:** A phrase, symbol, or symbols which indicate the manner in which a note or notes are to be played.

**Augmentation Dot:** A dot appearing just after a notehead ( ♩.) which adds half of the value of the note, to that note.

**Barline:** A vertical line or lines which divides a musical piece into measures.

**Beam:** A thick line or lines used to connect multiple consecutive Eighth Notes or notes of shorter values.

**BPM (or bpm):** An abbreviation for "Beats per Minute," and the measurement of Tempo in Metronomic Markings.

**Breath Mark:** A comma shaped notation ( 𝄒 ) written above the staff which indicates the best place to take a breath.

**Coda:** From the Italian meaning, "tail," a passage of no particular length that brings a musical piece to a conclusion.

**Cautionary Accidental:** An Accidental that is not musically necessary, but simply serves as a reminder.

**Chromatic Scale:** A scale with twelve pitches, with each one being a semi-tone (half-step) apart from the others.

**Clef:** A Music Symbol (such as 𝄞 ) appearing at the start of each staff which indicates the pitch of the written notes.

**Cresc.** or **Crescendo:** Meaning, "to become gradually stronger," it indicates an increase in volume.

**Cut Time:** Also referred to as Alla Breve, it is the equivilent of a 2/2 Time Signature and often used in Marches.

**Decresc.** or **Decrescendo:** Decrease the volume gradually as in Diminuendo, below.

**Dim.** or **Diminuendo:** Meaning, "to become gradually softer," it indicates a decrease in volume.

**Dominant Chord:** A chord, based on the fifth degree of the scale, which naturally tends to resolve to the tonic.

**Double Flat:** An Accidental ( ♭♭ ) which indicates that the note is to be lowered by 2 semi-tones (half-steps).

**Double Sharp:** An Accidental ( 𝄪 ) which indicates that the note is to be raised by 2 semi-tones (half-steps).

**Dynamics:** The volume of the overall sound or notes played and the changes in volume during the piece.

**Embouchure:** The manner in which the mouth and tongue are applied and conform to the mouthpiece.

**Enharmonic:** Notes or keys which are named differently, but will sound the same pitch when played.

**Flat Sign:** A music symbol ( ♭ ) appearing before a note which lowers the pitch by a semi-tone (half-step).

**Half-Step (Semi-Tone):** The interval (distance) between two notes which is equivilent to one-twelfth of an octave.

**Intensity:** One of the characteristics of a musical tone which is determined by the volume of the sound produced.

**Interval:** The relationship between two musical notes, usually classified by quality and distance.

**Key Signature:** A series of sharps or flats placed on the staff, indicating which notes are to be consistently altered.

**Ledger Line:** A short line written above or below the staff used to indicate notes which fall outside the staff's range.

**Legato:** Meaning, "tied together," (not to be confused with Tied Notes), play smoothly and with a soft attack.

**Lip Slur:** In wind instruments, a slur containing only notes which are played with identical fingerings.

**Lento:** A tempo indication meaning slowly, played within the range of approximately 40 - 60 bpm.

**Marcato:** Italian for "marked," an articulation ( $\wedge$ ) characterized by a forceful attack followed by a decay of the tone.

**Measure:** Also known as a bar, a segment of time defined by the Key Signature and separated by barlines.

**Meter:** The number of recurring beats in the piece, divided into measures, as indicated by the Time Signature.

**Metronome:** A device and practice aid which produces steady clicks at a Tempo set by the user.

**Metronomic Marking (M.M.):** Tempo indicator showing the number of beats per minute for a given note value.

**Moderato:** Meaning, "moderately," a Tempo between Andante and Allegro in the range of 108-120 bpm.

**Modulation:** The act of changing from one key to another within a piece of music.

**Natural Sign:** A music symbol ( ♮ ) appearing before a note which restores the note to it's unaltered state.

**Octave:** The interval (distance) between one note, and another note with either half or double it's frequency.

**Pitch:** One of the major attributes of a musical tone, based on frequency, which disguishes it from other tones.

**Presto:** Meaning, "quick or fast," it refers to a very fast Tempo in the range of approximately 168 - 200 bpm.

**Relative Keys (Major or Minor):** A Major or Minor Scale or Key which share the same Key Signature.

**Rit. or Ritard. or Ritardando:** Indicates a gradual slowing of the Tempo until the end or otherwise indicated.

**Rhythm:** Recurring motion or movement produced by a succession of stressed and un-stressed elements.

**Semi-Tone (Half-Step):** The interval (distance) between two notes which is equivalent to one-twelfth of an octave.

**Sharp Sign:** A music symbol ( ♯ ) appearing before a note which raises the pitch by a semi-tone (half-step).

**Simile:** Play or articulate the music that follows in a similar fashion to which it has been notated to that point.

**Slur:** The act of playing, or the musical symbol indicating that certain notes are to be played without separation.

**Staccato:** Meaning, "detached" ( • ), it signifies a note of shortened duration & separated from the notes that follow.

**Staff:** The set of 5 lines and 4 spaces representing different pitches, upon which musical notes are written.

**Syncopation:** A change in the normal flow of the rhythm, where a beat which is normally weak, is stressed.

**Tempo:** The speed at which a piece is to be played, indicated by either the Metronomic Marking or a Music Term.

**Tenuto:** From the Italian meaning, "to hold" ( — ), play the note with slight emphasis and hold for it's full value.

**Tie:** Notation connecting two notes of the same pitch indicating that the notes are to be played as a single note.

**Timbre:** Musical quality (as in notes by different instruments) which distinguishes it from notes of the same pitch.

**Time Signature:** Notation showing how many beats are in each measure, and which note value receives one beat.

**Tonic:** The pitch in any Key to which all of the other pitches resolve; the first Degree of the scale.

**Tone (Musical Tone):** A steady musical sound characterized by pitch, intensity, duration, and timbre.

**Vivace:** Meaning, "lively," it indicates a Tempo faster than Allegro in the range of approximately 140 - 168 bpm.

**Whole-step:** Also known as a "Whole Tone," the distance between two notes equal to 2 semi-tones (2 half-steps).

# TRUMPET FINGERING CHART

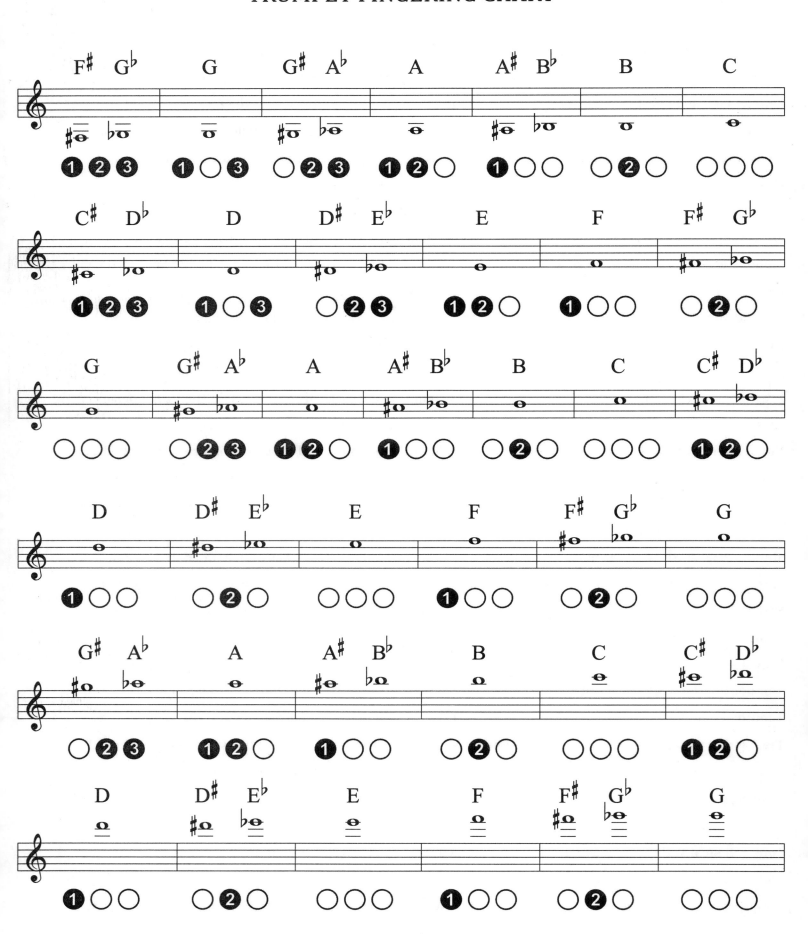